CLEOPATRA

by
Amy Wachspress, M.A.

Marjorie L. Kelley, Ed.D.
Educational Designer

Rae Ecklund
Illustrator

Quercus Corporation
2405 Castro Valley Boulevard
Castro Valley, California 94546

Printed in the United States of America.
ISBN 0-912925-81-7

Contents

Where Does Cleopatra's Story Start?   5

1: Cleopatra Meets Caesar 8

2: Cleopatra's New Friend 16

3: Cleopatra Rules Again 23

4: Cleopatra in Rome 32

5: A Message from Antony 39

6: Cleopatra Sails into Tarsus 43

7: Antony Meets Cleopatra 48

8: Antony in Egypt 55

9: Antony's Problems in Rome 60

10: Cleopatra Gets Married 67

11: Antony and Cleopatra in Egypt 72

12: War 82

13: A Death in Egypt 90

14: Octavian's Plans 101

15: The Final Days 107

Where Does Cleopatra's Story Start?

Cleopatra and her family were Greek. How did they wind up ruling Egypt? Let's take a quick look at what happened before this story starts.

When Alexander the Great of Greece died in 323 B.C., Egypt belonged to him. He left Egypt to one of his generals. This general made himself King of Egypt. After that, Egypt no longer belonged to Greece. This new King of Egypt was a good ruler. He kept the Greek love for beauty and ideas alive in Egypt. When he died, he passed Egypt down to his children.

Egypt stayed in this family for nearly 300 years. No one else in the family was as wise as that first King. Most of this family didn't care much about the Egyptians. They cared about money and power. Their love for power often caused them to kill their own family. Brothers, sisters, parents and children killed each other for Egypt's crown.

The last person in this family to rule Egypt was Cleopatra. She loved power too. But she was quite different from most of her family. She was very learned. She spoke seven languages. The Greek love for beauty and ideas was still alive in her. She liked to use her mind. She liked to have other people who thought about life around her. Many thinkers lived in Egypt, so Cleopatra was in good company. Surprisingly, after years of bad rulers, Egypt still had a lot to offer. Egypt was still a place of great learning and beauty.

When Cleopatra's father died, he left Egypt to Cleopatra and her brother. In those days, Egypt was one of the few countries still ruling itself. The Roman Empire ruled every country on the Mediterranean Sea except for Egypt.

Now let's go to the year 48 B.C. Julius Caesar and Pompey are two Roman generals. They are fighting over who should rule the Roman

Empire. Even though Caesar and Pompey are at war, they respect each other. They used to be friends. Caesar chases Pompey to the East. Pompey runs to Alexandria, Egypt. All of Egypt is ruled from the city of Alexandria.

Caesar follows Pompey to Egypt. But when Caesar enters Alexandria, he discovers that Pompey is dead. The King of Egypt presents Caesar with Pompey's head. What a mistake! Caesar never would have killed Pompey. He just wanted to take away Pompey's power. Caesar is very angry at this Egyptian boy King. This King is 16 years old.

Caesar learns that the King and Queen of Egypt are at war. The King has chased his sister to Arabia. Arabia is the land next to Egypt. Caesar wants to meet this Egyptian King's sister. Maybe this sister could help her brother be a better ruler.

Caesar knows it's very dangerous for this sister to return to Alexandria. Her brother wants to kill her. Caesar wonders how to bring her back to Alexandria safely. He decides to let her know he wants to meet her. Now our story is about to start. This Egyptian King's sister is, of course, Cleopatra.

1
Cleopatra
Meets Caesar

Cleopatra had run away to Arabia one night three years ago. She left Alexandria suddenly when her brother tried to kill her. Cleopatra's brother did everything the Egyptian leaders told him to do. He could not think for himself. These leaders could rule Egypt easily with him as King. But they had no power with Cleopatra as Queen. Cleopatra could think for herself. So these men wanted Cleopatra out of the picture.

Cleopatra had made friends with one of the Arabian Kings. She had been very straightforward with this King. He liked that. Cleopatra could speak the King's own language, too. The King was very pleased that Cleopatra had thought Arabic was worth learning. The King of Arabia liked Cleopatra so much that he joined her cause. He took his fighting men and went with Cleopatra to Egypt.

For months, Cleopatra and the Arabian King had been fighting against Cleopatra's brother. Their men fought along a sandy stretch of land. This land marked where Egypt and Arabia met. Cleopatra never went to the fight itself. She was still a girl of 19. So she stayed away from the fighting. She lived in a small town just outside of Egypt.

The townspeople felt very sorry for this young Queen. They could see her every morning when she walked across the sand. She would listen for hours to the distant fighting. Her hair was long and black. The wind made it wave like a flag. She was very tall. The Egyptian people said Cleopatra was the daughter of the gods. There was something about her that made you believe it was true. Everyone knew that this Queen cared about Egypt more than anything else. She wanted to go home.

When she stood and listened to the fighting, Cleopatra thought about Alexandria. She remembered her room in the palace. Was her room as she had left it? Were her old teachers still alive? She wondered which flowers were growing in the palace gardens. This war went on and on. Nothing was decided. She worried that the good Arabian King was getting tired of fighting. Cleopatra was starting to think she would never see her home again. But just when it seemed like nothing would ever change, something did change.

When Cleopatra left Egypt, she took a servant named Apollodorus with her. Apollodorus was the big man who protected Cleopatra. He had been given to her by her father when he died. Apollodorus was very strong. He was ten years older than Cleopatra. Even though he was a servant, he was like an uncle to Cleopatra. One day, he brought her the news that changed everything.

"Caesar has come to Alexandria," Apollodorus told Cleopatra. "He was chasing Pompey. Pompey is dead. Caesar has brought many Romans with him. There are enough Romans to take over Egypt. But they say Caesar is still deciding what he wants to do."

"Where is my brother?" Cleopatra asked.

"In Alexandria," Apollodorus said. "They say he thinks he can fight Caesar and win."

"My brother is about as smart as grass. It's a wonder we don't have to water him," Cleopatra joked. Apollodorus laughed. Cleopatra continued, "He will lose Egypt. That is what he will do." If her brother decided to fight with Caesar, he would certainly lose. If he decided not to fight Caesar, he would probably lose Egypt anyway. Caesar was a very learned man. Cleopatra's brother had never cared about learning anything. He also had no taste. He and Caesar were like night and day. Caesar would never leave Egypt to Cleopatra's brother. Caesar would make Egypt part of the Roman Empire.

"How can I save Egypt from the Romans?" Cleopatra asked Apollodorus. That night Cleopatra could not sleep. What could she do for Egypt from here? She was in Arabia.

Cleopatra was in luck. The very next day she got a message from Caesar. The message said that he wanted the fighting to stop. He would talk to Cleopatra's brother. He also wanted to meet Cleopatra. He would try to bring her back to Alexandria soon. He would let her know when it was safe to return. Cleopatra was sure Caesar would protect her if she went to him. But how could she reach him safely?

She sent for Apollodorus. "I must meet Caesar," Cleopatra said. "He wants to see me. I'm sure of that. And I can't wait for him to send for me." She lifted the corner of a rug that lay on the floor. "I have an idea that might work. We will take this rug to Caesar as a gift."

Apollodorus looked at the rug. It was very beautiful. It had gold and silver sewn through the cloth on the top. But Apollodorus looked worried. "Why will we take a rug to Caesar?" he asked.

"Because I will be rolled up inside of it," Cleopatra said. "Do you think you can carry me?"

"I have carried heavier loads than the Queen of Egypt," Apollodorus said. He laughed softly. "But none as great as this," he added.

So Cleopatra quietly left Arabia and headed home. When she got to Alexandria it was late in the day. Apollodorus carefully rolled her up in the rug and tied it. He walked out into the dark Alexandria street.

Apollodorus found two Egyptian guards at the front door to the palace. He told them he had brought a rug that Caesar wanted.

"Well lay it down," one guard said. "We'll have someone come get it."

"My orders are to bring it to Caesar myself," Apollodorus said.

"Wait here," the guard said.

Apollodorus thought about how much the Egyptian people loved Cleopatra. She would be a good queen. The guard returned with a well-dressed Roman. The Roman said, "Caesar has not ordered a rug."

Apollodorus didn't know what to do. He heard the Queen's voice whisper, "It's a gift." Apollodorus said, "Of course Caesar didn't order it—it's a gift." Cleopatra whispered again, "From Egypt's ruler." So Apollodorus said, "From Egypt's ruler." The Roman told him to wait again. When this Roman told Caesar Apollodorus' words, Caesar decided to see the rug.

Apollodorus went into the palace. What a way to come home, he thought to himself. He was led into Caesar's room. He carefully placed the rug on the floor. He bowed before Caesar and said, "A gift for Caesar from Egypt's Cleopatra." Apollodorus began to untie and unroll the rug.

"A beautiful gift," Caesar said. "But from Cleopatra? I thought it was from her brother—that boy King."

Just then a girl rolled out of the rug. She was wearing a white dress. She had a thin piece of gold around her head. Her black hair flashed like a basket of stars. And her eyes shot at Caesar like arrows of light. Caesar knew right away who she was. But before he could say anything, she spoke.

"I am Cleopatra, the Queen of Egypt," she said. "You must be Caesar." Cleopatra liked Caesar right away. He looked like a kind and wise ruler. His eyes were deep and full of thought. She smiled and held her hand out to him.

"What a clever idea," Caesar said. "I only wish I had thought of it! Wait until that younger

14

brother of yours hears of this." Caesar laughed. Then he said, "Caesar is most pleased to meet Queen Cleopatra." He took her hand. Cleopatra stepped off the rug as if the palace belonged to her again. It felt good to be home. She could tell that Caesar was very pleased to see her. She was sure that this great man would give Egypt back to her.

2

Cleopatra's New Friend

Only minutes after they met, Caesar and Cleopatra were talking like old friends. Caesar wanted to hear from Cleopatra what had happened in Egypt. Cleopatra explained that her brother made her run away to Arabia. This kind of thing happened all the time in her family. But Cleopatra knew that the people of Egypt wanted her to be Queen.

"It's not very fair," Cleopatra said. "My brother can't tell right from wrong. He has never even been to the great library here at Alexandria. It is the greatest library in the world. How can he pretend to care about Egypt? He has no care for Egypt's thinkers and artists. He does not even listen to music. All he cares about is power and money."

"And you don't care about power and money?" Caesar asked. Then Caesar laughed.

"Of course I do. What leader of a country does not care about these things? Can you say that you don't care about power or money? But I give a thought to other things too. Just like you do," Cleopatra said. "People come from all over the world to learn in Egypt. I want to see this continue and grow. Besides, my people want me to be Queen. Ask any Egyptian in the marketplace."

Caesar and Cleopatra talked for a long time. Cleopatra told Caesar everything that she was angry about. But she let him know she would respect his decisions. Whatever he thought best for Egypt, she would do. He was a lot older than she. He was in his 50's. He was the ruler of Rome. He would know the best thing to do.

Caesar was very pleased with Cleopatra. He loved to watch her face as she talked. She felt strongly about the things she spoke of. He could feel that she had thought about what she wanted to say. She also spoke Latin, Caesar's language, in a very beautiful, musical way. It was quite pleasant to listen to her. He wanted to spend more time with this bright girl Queen. He decided that he would see that she was given back her crown.

That night Cleopatra slept in her own room in the palace. Caesar placed guards around her door. Her brother had not cared about Cleopatra's things at all. Her room was still as she left it over three years ago! She touched the pictures on her walls. The books she was reading three years ago were still on her table. That night she slept soundly for the first time in years.

For his part, Caesar had never met a girl quite like this one. Egypt would be lucky to have such a ruler. Caesar would make Cleopatra's brother give Cleopatra back her crown. There had to be a way to make these two get along. Caesar thought maybe he should stay in Egypt a little while. Then he could be sure this King and Queen worked out their problems. Caesar had to laugh at himself. He really cared about Egypt. But he was also thinking of a way to see more of Cleopatra!

The next morning, Caesar met with Cleopatra's brother. Cleopatra was right about him. This boy King could not even think for himself. He brought a powerful Egyptian man with him to see Caesar. This man helped the King decide things. To Caesar, it looked like this man really did most of the deciding. Cleopatra's brother puffed himself up to look big. Then he whispered back and forth to this man. He asked this man what to say.

Caesar listened to what the boy King said against Cleopatra. Caesar asked him things from time to time. Then Caesar told him that Egypt could continue to rule itself. Egypt need not fear Rome. But only if Cleopatra was given her crown back. Caesar wanted to see brother and sister rule together.

Cleopatra's brother acted like a child when he heard this. He kicked his feet. He jumped up and wagged his finger at Caesar. He talked angrily in a high, scratchy voice. Caesar wondered how this child could be in the same family as Cleopatra.

"I will meet with you and your sister together tonight," Caesar said.

"My sister is in Arabia," the King said.

"Your sister is in her room here at the palace," Caesar told him.

The boy's face turned almost blue. "She is not supposed to be here!" he cried.

"Well luckily, she is here," Caesar replied. And with that he sent this unpleasant boy away. Then he called Cleopatra to him.

Today Cleopatra wore a deep blue dress with bits of silver in it. Some small green stones circled her neck. She still wore that thin gold crown around her head. She knew how much Caesar loved beauty. So Cleopatra had dressed with care.

Caesar stood up when Cleopatra entered the room. Was this the girl who rolled out of a rug the night before? How different she looked. She looked older. She looked more like a woman. Caesar was even more pleased with her when he saw her today.

"Let's say I have only one afternoon in Alexandria," Caesar said. "What should I visit?"

Cleopatra didn't even think for a second.

"The library," she said. "Great thinkers come from all over the world to learn at this library."

"Then let's go," Caesar said.

So Cleopatra and Caesar went to the library. Cleopatra showed him many writings there. Some were on paper, but others were cut in stone. She seemed especially excited by the things about the stars and the sky. She explained things to him in Latin. No matter what language something was written in, Cleopatra could read it. Caesar wondered how Cleopatra had found the time to learn all these languages. She was still so young.

"I believe there are mysteries in the sky," Cleopatra told Caesar. "There are things we can know about our lives written in the stars. I want to figure some of these things out before I die. I want to learn about the powers we know so little about."

Caesar lost all track of time in the great library. He noticed the order of things there. It was a very good way to make things easy to find. It gave him some good ideas for the library in Rome.

As Caesar and Cleopatra were leaving the

library, Apollodorus came running to them. "I am sorry to bring bad news, my Queen," Apollodorus said. "Egypt's King has a trap waiting for Caesar at the palace. They plan to kill Caesar. The King's men are armed for a fight."

"Thank you, Apollodorus," Cleopatra said. Then she turned to Caesar. "I am sorry that my brother makes Egypt so unpleasant for you."

"I would face ten such brothers," Caesar replied. "To spend one afternoon with one sister such as you." Then he called his guards. He sent word to his men. He prepared to fight this King.

3

Cleopatra Rules Again

Caesar left Cleopatra at the library. He left guards to protect her. She would be safe there. He promised to send her news of what was happening.

Caesar sent Cleopatra a message within the hour. Cleopatra's brother had learned that Caesar had discovered his plans. Caesar's men were heading toward the palace. So Cleopatra's brother ran away from the palace. He took all his men and ran to his ships on the waterfront. Egyptians were especially good at fighting at sea in ships. It was safe for Cleopatra to return to the palace, the message said. The fighting had moved to the waterfront.

Cleopatra returned to the palace at once. She knew she would be able to see the fighting from there. The palace was on a hill. If Caesar killed her brother, Cleopatra would have her crown to herself. Yet all she could think about was Caesar! "What is wrong with me?" Cleopatra asked herself. "These men are fighting over my right to the crown. Here I am thinking about Caesar from Rome instead of my Egypt."

From the palace, Cleopatra could see the ships on the waterfront. There were men fighting along the shoreline. She could not tell who was winning. By now it was getting dark quickly. Then light started to come from the Egyptian ships. It took Cleopatra a moment to figure out what was happening. The light was fire. The Egyptian ships were burning. How clever of Caesar. He was burning his enemy's ships. Cleopatra felt strange. She was watching all the Egyptian fighting ships burn and she was pleased. The Egyptians on the ships all jumped off into the water.

But very soon Cleopatra was not pleased anymore. The fire was spreading from the ships to the shore. The great library overlooked the sea. It stood very near the water. Cleopatra rubbed her eyes and looked again. Her eyes were not mistaken—the library was on fire. Cleopatra watched as the greatest treasure of Egypt burned. There was nothing she could do about it.

Cleopatra sat up all night. By morning, next to nothing was left of the beautiful library. But also by morning Cleopatra was the ruler of Egypt. Her brother had jumped from a burning ship during the fight. He could not swim with his heavy war clothes on. The water swallowed him up.

Caesar returned to the palace tired but excited. Cleopatra was so happy to see him alive. She threw her arms around his neck before thinking about it. Caesar was surprised but quite pleased.

"I'm very happy to return your crown to you," Caesar said to Cleopatra.

Cleopatra ordered the rest of her enemies to be killed right away. "I don't want to take any chances," she told Caesar. Next she ordered gifts to be sent to her friend, the Arabian King. Then she noticed how sad Caesar looked.

"What is wrong?" Cleopatra asked him.

"I'm very sorry that we burned down the library," Caesar said. "How lucky for me that you took me to see it. Now it's gone. I didn't come to Egypt to make war."

"Egypt was already at war," Cleopatra told Caesar. "Remember that my brother and I were fighting. Had there been no war then perhaps Caesar would never have met Cleopatra. Will you leave Egypt now that the war is over?" Cleopatra asked.

Caesar smiled. "What is there to keep me here?" he asked.

In a very quiet voice, Cleopatra said, "Me."

Her voice was quiet, but Cleopatra's signal was loud. Caesar was not a man to waste time. And Cleopatra had never been any good at waiting around. They were married within the week. Now Caesar already had a wife back in Rome. But we must remember that all this happened in Egypt in 48 B.C. People followed the laws of the time. The law said a man could have more than one wife at once. In Rome a man could only have one wife at a time. But now Caesar was in Egypt—following Egyptian laws. Caesar and Cleopatra were in love too. Caesar thought he would worry about the Roman laws when he returned home.

After they were married, Caesar wanted to sail up the Nile River. He wanted to see more of Egypt. So Cleopatra ordered a special ship to be made ready. In the meantime, she showed Caesar some other sights in Alexandria. They visited the lighthouse. This lighthouse was one of the seven wonders of the world. They also visited a monument to Alexander the Great. Alexander the Great was buried in this monument. In his own life, Caesar tried to be like Alexander. So it was very special for him to visit this monument. There was so much to see in Alexandria. Caesar also found the city itself very beautiful.

The Romans whispered that Cleopatra was using magic to trap Caesar in Egypt. But Caesar had not had much time off in years. He knew he would have to go back to Rome soon. He would have to go fight again soon. Maybe he would die. So just for a few months, he wanted to take a break. He was in love with his new wife. He was 55 years old. Cleopatra made Caesar feel young again.

When their ship was ready, Caesar and Cleopatra headed down the Nile. Cleopatra had pictures of Greek gods painted on the walls of their rooms. She had brought some of the best actors from Alexandria with them. Each night they watched a different play. Sometimes Caesar and Cleopatra would take parts in these plays. Sometimes they read out loud to each other. They listened to a lot of music also. They stopped at towns along the Nile often. Then they went to look at monuments or gardens or whatever they found. Everyone was sad on the day the ship turned around. It was time to return to Alexandria.

On their first night back in Alexandria, Cleopatra and Caesar took a walk. They walked through the palace gardens. The moonlight looked like silver fire on the treetops. Caesar took Cleopatra's hand. "These have been the best months of my life," Caesar said. "Egypt is a magical land. But now I must return home."

"Egypt will miss you," Cleopatra told Caesar.

"How would Egypt like to come to Rome?" Caesar asked.

Cleopatra and Caesar sail down the Nile.

"Egypt would love to go to Rome," Cleopatra replied.

Caesar told Cleopatra his plans. "I must return to Rome by land. I must see that everything is in order here in the East. When I am back in Rome, I will prepare a house for you. Then I will send for you. You can come quickly by sea."

"I will come to you by sea," Cleopatra said. "But I will not come quickly. You will have to wait at least a year."

"Why?" Caesar asked.

Cleopatra smiled. "Because I would not take a little baby on such a long trip."

"What little baby?" Caesar asked. "I don't see a little baby."

"Ours. You don't see it because it isn't born yet." Cleopatra said.

Caesar had been married several times in his life. But he only had one child and she died at a young age. Now he could not believe his ears. "Is it true?" Caesar cried.

"Very true. It is a gift from the gods," Cleopatra said. "The gods of Egypt have taken to you, Caesar. They are looking after you."

Caesar was a Roman. He was supposed to believe in Roman gods. But he didn't believe much in any gods. Suddenly, he thought maybe there really were gods. He could not guess if they were Egyptian or Roman. But someone's gods had sent Cleopatra to Caesar. Now they were sending him a child.

Many months after Caesar left Egypt, he was still not back in Rome. He had discovered problems in the Eastern Roman Empire. He had to fight some wars. He was fighting a war when he got a message from Alexandria. A son had been born to him in Egypt. Cleopatra had named their son Caesarion, which means little Caesar.

4

Cleopatra in Rome

Caesar had a special house built for Cleopatra and Caesarion. It was on the outer edge of Rome. It was small but very beautiful. There were trees all the way around the house. Caesar even had gardens planted just for Cleopatra. Caesar came to Cleopatra's house often. It was a place for him to get away and rest. Besides, Caesar wanted to spend time with Caesarion. Caesar was very proud of this son of his. He was a beautiful baby and very smart. Caesar was happy to have his Egyptian family in Rome.

Cleopatra was glad to be with her husband

again. But she didn't like Rome. It was ugly to her. She didn't feel safe in Rome either. She could tell right away that the Romans didn't like her. She heard that they called her "the Egyptian witch."

Caesar asked Cleopatra for her ideas about problems he had ruling Rome. She often thought of helpful things to tell Caesar. Caesar was glad to have a wife who knew about ruling a country. Caesar made many changes for the good of Rome's people at this time. Many of these changes were probably Cleopatra's ideas. But the Romans didn't see it this way. They didn't like the power Cleopatra had over Caesar. The leaders of Rome were quite unhappy with Cleopatra. They refused to think of her as Caesar's wife.

So Cleopatra never went out in Rome. She stayed at her house. Caesar told the Roman leaders they could not go visit Cleopatra. Only the artists and thinkers could go to Cleopatra's house. Many learned men and women visited Cleopatra. They found her to be very different from what they had heard. Cleopatra had brought some learned men of Egypt to Rome with her. She had brought her own reader of stars. Her house was always filled with lively talk.

Cleopatra had also brought a new lady-in-waiting with her. She had picked her especially for this trip. Her name was Charmian. She was the same age as Cleopatra. Charmian was a large, dark brown woman. She was very strong. She wore about 20 gold earrings on the outside edge of each ear. Charmian was kind and she had an eye for beauty. If she placed flowers on the table, they would look perfect. She was also very smart. Cleopatra and Charmian often read together. Charmian already knew more than most servants from being so close to Cleopatra. Cleopatra was in a strange land, far from home. Charmian became more than a servant to her—she was her friend.

One day Cleopatra and Charmian were sitting on the grass in the garden. Caesarion was playing with some toys. He was singing to himself. Charmian was doing some sewing. Without looking up from her work, Charmian said, "What is on your mind?"

Cleopatra was surprised. "What do you

mean?" she asked.

"Something is bothering you. Did you think I would not notice?" Charmian asked. "I am worried about you, my Queen."

"You are right, of course," Cleopatra said. "I do have something bothering me. I keep wondering why Caesar has not named Caesarion as his heir. The Romans don't even think I'm Caesar's wife. We were married under Egyptian law. Caesar should make his people think of me as his wife. I have been here two years now. Caesarion has almost never left this house and these grounds. Yet Caesarion should rule all of Rome some day. Instead, Caesar takes that Octavian with him everywhere."

"Isn't Caesar Octavian's uncle?" Charmian asked.

"Yes. Octavian is the son of Caesar's dead brother. He is only 17. Octavian was Caesar's heir before Caesarion was born. But Caesar acts as though nothing has changed. He still trains Octavian to rule one day. I have never met Octavian. But I don't like what I hear of him. They say he only cares about money. But he does not like to spend it. He only likes to have it," Cleopatra said.

"Ask Caesar what he plans to do about Caesarion," Charmian said.

"I have already. He says he is writing a new will. He says he plans to have Caesarion named the heir of Rome. But he must wait until the child is older. He says it is unsafe and unwise to do it now. With Caesar's protection, how is it unsafe?" Cleopatra asked.

"He knows Rome better than we do. If he says it is unsafe, it probably is," Charmian replied. "Remember that Caesar loves Caesarion. Don't worry, my Queen."

"I am not the only one who is worried. Some of the wise men who came with us from Egypt are worried. My star reader says there have been strange lights in the sky. The gods are trying to tell us something. I am afraid," Cleopatra told Charmian.

"Have you told Caesar about the messages in the sky?" Charmian asked.

"He does not believe in such things," Cleopatra said. "I have seen the shooting stars. They must mean something."

It certainly seemed like the stars were sending a message. Many people in Rome believed these stars. Many people were telling Caesar to be careful. But Caesar said it was useless to worry about death. Death would come in its time whether Caesar worried about it or not.

Charmian came rushing back from the marketplace crying one day. Cleopatra guessed what had happened already.

"Caesar has been stabbed," Charmian cried. "He is dead. The whole city is in an uproar. It's terrible. No one knows what will happen now. Rome is like a barn burning with animals in it."

"Bring Caesarion to me," Cleopatra said. Then she looked out her window across Rome. Caesar was a great Roman general and ruler. But Cleopatra was remembering him as a man. She remembered him talking with the learned men of Egypt late at night. She thought of him riding a horse. She remembered him tipping his head to catch the sun on his face. Cleopatra's husband was dead.

For one week after Caesar's death, the night sky put on a show. There were shooting stars and strange, bright lights. But now Cleopatra knew the meaning of these things. Caesar's life had changed the world. The stars were marking the passing of this great man.

5
A Message from Antony

Caesar had kept an eye out for Egypt. Now Cleopatra had no one to count on in Rome. No one who was anyone cared about Egypt or Cleopatra. Cleopatra had friends in Rome. But they were mostly artists and thinkers. Caesar had kept the powerful people in Rome away from Cleopatra's house. Cleopatra didn't feel safe in Rome anymore. She was afraid someone would try to kill Caesarion. He was Caesar's only living child. Caesar's will named Octavian as his heir. Maybe Octavian would try to kill Caesarion. So Cleopatra said goodbye to her few friends in Rome. Then she sailed back to Egypt.

It was so nice to come home. Her people were glad to see Cleopatra safe and sound. When the ship touched the shore, the Egyptians blew horns. They rang bells. They played music. The Egyptians were happy to have their Queen back home. And Alexandria had never looked more beautiful to Cleopatra.

Cleopatra had left Egypt with big dreams for her son. But now that Caesar was dead, she gave up these dreams. She would just try to keep Egypt safe from the new Roman rulers.

Meanwhile, the Romans fought it out among themselves. They chased each other from country to country, fighting each other. There were two Roman generals who had really liked Caesar as a ruler. One of them, of course, was Octavian. Octavian was young, but he did not play games. You could not put anything past him. He knew Mark Antony was also very unhappy to see Caesar dead. Antony had been Caesar's chief general when they went fighting. He was the smartest general living. So Octavian asked Antony to join with him. Together they hunted down and killed the men who stabbed Caesar. One by one they got them all. This took them about two years.

After they killed Caesar's enemies, Octavian and Antony went different ways. Octavian returned to Rome to look after the home front. Now he was 19, and he ruled the strongest country in the world! Antony prepared for more wars. He was making his way in an eastern direction. He slowly took over more and more land for Rome to own.

Cleopatra was worried. It was only a matter of time before Antony would march into Egypt. She didn't want a war. Antony had respected Caesarion as Caesar's rightful son in Rome. Would he still care about Caesarion? Or would he want to kill him to please Octavian? What could Cleopatra do to win Antony to her cause? What could she do to protect her son? Before Cleopatra thought of anything to do, Antony made a move.

Antony sent his friend Dellius to Alexandria. Dellius told Cleopatra she must go to see Antony right away. Antony wanted to know what Cleopatra was doing in Rome when Caesar died. Antony wondered if Cleopatra was in on the plan to kill Caesar! Cleopatra could not believe anyone thought she had helped kill Caesar. Why would she do such a thing?

Dellius liked Cleopatra right away. He felt bad bringing her such a mean message. Dellius said, "Antony is a very friendly man. Don't be afraid of him. A kinder man never won a war. Dress up in your finest clothes for him. Show him you are a powerful queen. He will not harm you or Egypt. I know Antony well. The words I speak of him are true. He is a paper tiger. He seems more dangerous than he is."

Dellius explained that Antony was in Tarsus. Tarsus was a city nearby across the sea. Dellius said that a river ran from the sea straight into Tarsus. So Cleopatra could sail all the way to Tarsus. She ordered a special ship to be built right away. She believed everything Dellius told her. She would do as he said. She would give Antony a show he would never forget.

6
Cleopatra Sails into Tarsus

The people of Tarsus had never seen anything like it. They ran from the river into town and back. Word spread like fire. People closed down their shops and went to the river to look. They took their children down to the water to see this sight.

A large, flat ship sailed slowly and lazily up the river. The whole ship was painted gold. The sails were a deep, rich purple color. They were so purple, they made you want to eat something that purple. Egyptian men in silver clothes were rowing the ship with silver oars. The sun licked

43

the silver oars as they moved. You could not tell where the shiny oars ended and the water began. It looked like ladders of light climbing from the water to the ship.

Egyptian music made its way to the shore. The people of Tarsus had never heard Egyptian music before. It sounded strange and wonderful. After a while, the smell of flowers whispered in the air. People figured out that the beautiful smell came from the ship. A dream ship had come to Tarsus. And on this dream ship was the Queen of Egypt.

Cleopatra was lying down on a thick, black cloth. A gold cloth stretched over her head to keep the sun off. She wore a rich purple dress and a lot of gold and silver. She even had gold on her feet—and no shoes. Charmian sat just behind her. She wore a beautiful red dress.

Soon Antony's men came down to the river from the palace. The marketplace was empty. The palace was empty. Everyone was at the waterfront. Antony was left alone sitting in the palace.

Now Antony had sent Dellius to bring Cleopatra to Tarsus a while ago. But Cleopatra needed time to prepare for the show she was putting on. She didn't rush off to meet Antony. Antony sent her letters and finally ordered her to Tarsus. But she didn't come until she was ready. Antony thought she was making fun of him. He felt like a clown. So he refused to go watch her ship sailing up the river.

Then Dellius came to see Antony. They were old friends. "You are missing a prize sight," Dellius said. "This is no time to be proud or angry. Some day, you will be friends with this magical Queen. Then you will wish that you saw this sight."

Antony really did want to see the show. So he told Dellius to take a boat and row out to Cleopatra. "Tell her that I'm pleased that she finally came to Tarsus. Invite her to supper."

Cleopatra saw Dellius rowing out to meet her. She stopped and waited for him. By now the sun was starting to go down.

"Where is Antony?" Cleopatra asked Dellius.

"He thinks you are making fun of him," Dellius replied. "Don't worry, though. He will change his mind. He sent me to invite you to supper."

"Tell him my cooks are already preparing food for him here. Invite him to eat with me instead," Cleopatra told Dellius.

Meanwhile, Antony had let himself take just a peek out the window. He saw all the gold and silver on Cleopatra's ship. Then it hit him that he had invited the Egyptian Queen for supper. But all his cooks were down at the waterfront watching this Queen!

When Dellius returned to Antony, he found him in the palace kitchen. "What food will I give her? Call my cooks quickly." This man had won many wars—and Cleopatra had him worried about supper!

"Don't worry," Dellius said. "She asked me to invite you to eat with her instead."

"What good luck!" Antony said.

Cleopatra saw Antony come down to the shore and get into a boat. "Well Charmian," she said, "now our work really begins." Cleopatra had her men row out to meet Antony. Then she pulled her last trick out of the bag.

It was getting dark quickly. Cleopatra wanted Antony to be sure to see her ship. She had brought special lights with her. These lights were tied onto large tree branches. When she gave the word, her servants lifted hundreds of lights at once. Suddenly the river was as bright as day around Cleopatra's ship. The silver and gold jumped across the water. The purple sails flew against the sky. The sky was that perfect clean blue color. That color you see sometimes right after the sun goes down.

The people of Tarsus could not believe their eyes. When those wonderful lights went up, everyone gasped. Then they started to clap. Antony's boat pulled up next to Cleopatra's ship. The people of Tarsus said it seemed like two gods were meeting.

7
Antony Meets Cleopatra

As Antony stepped onto the ship, Cleopatra held her hand out to him. She had purple and blue flowers in her shiny, black hair. When she moved toward him, she fairly danced. Her eyes were large and looked light purple. They were really gray—but Antony would soon discover that they changed color. They looked purple now because of Cleopatra's purple dress. She was tall and every inch a queen. Antony bowed and took her hand.

"I am very happy to meet you at last," Cleopatra said. "My husband spoke of you

Cleopatra, Queen of Egypt, meets Antony at Tarsus.

often. You were a good friend to him. I'm sure you miss him as I do. I wish he had brought you to our house in Rome."

Like most of Rome, Antony had not thought of Cleopatra as Caesar's wife. He suddenly felt terrible about making Cleopatra come to Tarsus. Why would she help kill a husband she loved? Antony could not bring himself to ask her about it. He could see that she was very unhappy that Caesar was dead. Antony was the kind of person who spoke his mind. He said, "I, too, wish that we had met in Rome. If we had, I would not have ordered you to Tarsus like this. I would have shown you more respect. We Romans have not been kind to you."

"I know that they said I caused Caesar's downfall in Rome. Many of his followers turned against him because they didn't like me. But I gave Caesar much happiness. Should the leaders of the world be kept from having any happiness? The Romans should have thanked me just for giving Caesar a son." Cleopatra was silent for a second. "Now I must say I'm sorry to you. I forget myself. I have left you standing and made you listen to my talk. Come onto my ship. Come eat the food we have prepared."

So Antony and Cleopatra sat down together. Antony was not disappointed with the food. It was wonderful.

Cleopatra could see that Antony was quite different from Caesar. Caesar had been a man of the mind. He could act quickly, but he liked to think about things. Antony was not a thinker or a learned man. But he was smart. He had been to many countries. He said whatever came into his head. Cleopatra thought he was like a big, friendly bear. She felt safe in his company. She had not felt so safe since she was a child. She liked him very much.

As they ate, Cleopatra told Antony some stories about Caesar and Caesarion. Many things that her little son did showed him to be Caesar's child. She thought back to her days in Rome. She remembered many stories to tell about people Antony knew. Caesar's last few months in power had been happy for Antony. Since Caesar's death, Antony had not let himself think about those times. Cleopatra brought those months back to him. At last he didn't feel sad thinking about that time. He could remember that time and his friend Caesar gladly.

When they finished eating, Cleopatra had actors and singers put on a show. It was a funny show with lots of good music. Antony had a great time.

When the food was gone and the show was over, Antony stayed on. He told stories about his trips throughout the world. He made Cleopatra laugh until it hurt. Cleopatra made Charmian tell some of her jokes. Charmian was great at telling jokes. She and Antony had a contest. The jokes stopped being funny after a while but they all laughed anyway.

Before they knew it, the sun was coming up. So Antony invited Cleopatra to join him in Tarsus for breakfast! Cleopatra wondered if this man ever slept. She promised to join Antony for supper—but she needed some sleep. She just about had to kick Antony off her ship.

Cleopatra stayed in Tarsus for two weeks. Then she decided it was time to go home. She had work waiting for her in Alexandria. She hated to leave Antony. He made her feel so good about things. She was always happy with him around. So she was sad to say goodbye to her new friends.

Antony was 41 years old. He had been to many countries. He had been married several times. He had met a lot of women. But no woman could even come close to Cleopatra. She was the brightest star in the sky. They said she used magic to keep Caesar in Egypt. Antony could believe that. Maybe that magic was working on him now. Antony could not stand to see Cleopatra go away.

Cleopatra sailed out of Tarsus early in the morning. She looked back at the city. She would miss her fun-loving Roman friend. Suddenly she noticed a boat heading quickly toward her ship. She turned to Charmian and said, "That looks like Antony."

Charmian looked at the boat. "That is Antony," Charmian said.

Sure enough, it was Antony. He caught up with them and climbed onto their ship. "Could I catch a ride to Egypt with you ladies?" Antony asked. Everyone laughed at him. But they took him with them. He sent for his men and had his things brought to Alexandria.

Antony's men had been about to go to war in the East. Antony's wife was starting fights with

Octavian back in Rome. Antony paid no attention to any of these things. He just made a beeline for Egypt. Antony was falling in love. And what about Cleopatra?

8

Antony in Egypt

Cleopatra was all ready to show Antony around Alexandria. She could think of many places to take him. But Antony had a few surprises for her. First of all, Antony presented Cleopatra with a honey-colored horse. Then he gave her a ring and some beautiful cloth. He ordered the cloth to be made into clothes right away. Cleopatra liked having so many gifts given to her all at once. Next, Antony told Cleopatra what he wanted to do in Alexandria. He didn't want to go sightseeing much. He wanted to play.

Antony and Cleopatra went hunting,

swimming, sailing and riding together. When Antony practiced fighting, Cleopatra went to watch. Cleopatra had never met a man who could keep going on so little sleep. It was hard for her to keep up with him. She tried to anyway.

Antony decided to teach Cleopatra one of his best games. They would dress up in lowly servants' clothes. Then they would go play tricks on the Egyptian people. The learned men of Egypt thought this was terrible. "This kind of thing does not suit a queen," they said. But for once, Cleopatra didn't care what they thought. Cleopatra and Antony usually played this game at night. The Egyptian people thought this was great fun. Cleopatra was the very first person in her family to ever speak Egyptian. For 300 years her family had spoken only Greek! The Egyptian people loved her even more for learning their language.

The people knew when Antony and Cleopatra were playing tricks on them. It was not hard to know who they were, even when they dressed in servants' clothes. The Egyptians liked Antony. He was a good laugh. In fact, Egypt was falling in love with Antony.

Meanwhile, Rome was falling out of love with Antony. His wife kept fighting small wars with Octavian. People said she was causing problems to make Antony come home. She didn't like him running around with Cleopatra. If she made enough problems in Rome, Antony would have to come home. Antony kept getting messages about what was happening. But he didn't care. He was having too much fun in Egypt.

One of the things Cleopatra liked best was going fishing. Antony knew how to fish, but he was not very good at it. He went fishing with Cleopatra two days in a row and caught nothing. Cleopatra caught a lot of fish. But Antony had no luck with a fishing pole.

On the third day fishing, Antony used a trick. He had his men swim under the boat. Then they put fish that Cleopatra had caught already on Antony's line. Cleopatra pretended she was very happy Antony was finally catching some fish. But really she had figured out what was happening.

The next day, Cleopatra made Antony go fishing again. Then Cleopatra had her men put a smoked fish on Antony's line. It was all cooked and ready to eat! When Antony pulled that fish in everyone laughed at him. He even laughed at himself. "I should have known you would figure out what I did," Antony said. The Egyptians would not let him forget that fish.

That night he went out in servants' clothes to play tricks. Everywhere he went, people asked, "Did you hear about Antony and the fish?" He just laughed and went back to the palace early. He threw stones at Cleopatra's window. When she came out he started to sing. He pretended to play music and howled, "I love you."

"Go to sleep, you silly Roman," Cleopatra called to him laughing. She closed her window. Antony went to bed.

The next day one of the most learned men of Egypt visited Cleopatra. "Can't you see how bad for you this Roman is?" this man asked. "You spend all your time with Antony. You go to parties. You never take time to think and learn anymore. You crawl through the streets in rags and play childish tricks. You are no longer acting like a queen."

Cleopatra became terribly angry. She ordered this man to be sent out of Egypt. Who did he think he was? No one could tell Cleopatra she didn't act like a queen. This man had been one of the wisest men in Alexandria. He had lived in Egypt his whole life. Cleopatra had often called on him to help her decide things. The next day her anger had passed. But this wise man could not be found. He had run away in fear for his life.

Cleopatra locked herself in her room. What have I done? she asked herself. This wise man is right. Antony is not good for me. But I can't help myself, Cleopatra thought. She cried for a long time. She was in love with Antony. It was nothing like the easy, friendly love she had with Caesar. Cleopatra could not stay away from Antony if she tried. She could not help herself. He held her attention like a fire. Queen or no queen, there was nothing she could do to change this.

9

Antony's Problems in Rome

One day Cleopatra found Antony reading letters from Rome. He didn't look pleased. Antony said, "My wife keeps fighting with Octavian. Now Octavian is angry with me. This letter is from him. He wonders if I care about Rome. He wants to know if I ever plan to come back to Rome."

Cleopatra looked at the floor. "Do you?" she asked quietly.

"Of course. I have to go home sometime," Antony said. "But I'll stay in Egypt as long as I can. Cleopatra—even if I go away, I can still come back."

The next day, a Roman sailed into Alexandria with bad news. Antony's wife was dead. Who would take care of Antony's house and his land? Most of all, who would take care of his children? Antony had to return to Rome right away.

That night, Cleopatra walked in the garden with Antony. "I am an Egyptian and you are a Roman. How can we be together?" Cleopatra asked.

"There must be a way," Antony replied. "I promise I will come back and marry you, Cleopatra. Caesarion should have his part of the Roman Empire. He is Caesar's son. At least he can help me rule the East. I will think of something. I will return soon."

The next morning Cleopatra watched from the palace as Antony's ship sailed away. It got smaller and smaller. Then it disappeared. Cleopatra felt like someone sadly waking from a wonderful dream.

The learned men of Egypt were very happy to see Antony go. Cleopatra had done little other than have a good time for months. They could see that Antony was not good for the Queen. He wanted to play all the time. Once he left, Cleopatra turned back to her old ways. She went back to work for the good of Egypt.

When Antony got back to Rome, he went to see Octavian. Antony was the only other Roman ruler at the time. Octavian felt that Antony had too much power. But what could Octavian do? The Roman people loved Antony. Octavian knew that Antony loved Cleopatra. And Cleopatra was the mother of Caesarion. Octavian feared that Caesarion would try to rule Rome one day. He feared Antony would help Caesarion do this. So Octavian wanted to take away some of Antony's power. How could he do this?

Octavian tried to get at Antony through Cleopatra. He knew that the Romans didn't like Cleopatra. They said she was a witch. She used magic to trap Caesar and now Antony. Many people thought she had caused Caesar's death by turning Rome against him. She had been a mystery to most people while in Rome. Many people fear things they don't know about. The Romans were afraid of Cleopatra. They were not used to seeing such a powerful woman. They feared her powers. Most of the Roman leaders were men. It bothered the Romans to see a woman ruler. Octavian used this feeling against Cleopatra in Rome. He used it to tear Antony down. Octavian kept saying bad things about Cleopatra and Egypt.

When Antony went to see Octavian, they got into a fight. Antony didn't want Octavian saying bad things about Cleopatra. Octavian said all Antony cared about was Egypt. He said Antony had no right to be a Roman ruler. Antony told Octavian he saw right through him. "You want to be the only ruler in the Roman Empire," Antony said. Then Antony walked out.

Antony went to see his friend Dellius. He had not seen Dellius since they had been in Tarsus together.

"My old friend," Dellius said, "what has come over you?"

"It's not hard to figure out," Antony replied. "I'm in love with the Queen of Egypt. I am a Roman ruler. She must look after her people. I must look after mine. I will not let Octavian make me look bad. I am a Roman general. I love Rome. Can't I be a friend of Egypt without being an enemy of Rome?"

"Open your eyes, Antony," Dellius said. "Egypt is a danger to Octavian as long as Caesarion lives."

"Of course," Antony said. "You are right. Octavian will not leave Egypt alone until Caesarion is dead. Octavian knows Caesarion has more right to rule Rome than Octavian. Caesarion is Caesar's true son!"

"Antony, to Romans you seem to care more about Egypt right now. I know that is not true," Dellius added quickly. "But that is what it looks like. Do something to show the Romans that you are still a Roman."

"Like what?" Antony asked.

Dellius answered carefully. "If I were you, I would try to get along with Octavian. He has been here ruling while you have been away in Egypt playing."

Antony saw that Dellius was right. So he went to see Octavian again. He asked Octavian what to do to show he was still a Roman.

Octavian had a sister named Octavia. He

loved her more than anything. She was very sweet and kind. The Roman people loved her too. If she married Antony, she would be the first lady of Rome. Octavian wanted this for her a lot. He also wanted to keep Antony out of Egypt. So he told Antony to marry his sister and take care of her. If Antony did this, then Antony could rule the Eastern Roman Empire himself. Octavian and Antony would cut the Empire in half.

If Antony said "no," he could lose everything. The Roman people loved Octavia. They would not like it if he refused to marry her. He would probably have to fight for his rights as a Roman ruler. And he didn't want his men to fight Octavian's. Romans fighting against Romans was not good for Rome. But if he said "yes," and married this woman, what would Cleopatra think? He had better try to forget Cleopatra. He was a Roman. She was an Egyptian.

Cleopatra was reading late one night. There was a knock at the door. It was Apollodorus. He said, "I wanted to tell you before you hear it somewhere else. Antony married Octavia in Rome. Octavia is Octavian's sister. Certainly Antony had to do this to keep his power. He probably did this also for the good of Rome."

"Probably. Thank you, Apollodorus, good night," Cleopatra said shakily. The next day Cleopatra burned all the clothes Antony had given her. She burned his letters. She threw away anything that would make her think of him. She told herself that this was just as well. Antony was not good for her. Egypt's learned men said this was the best thing to happen to Cleopatra. They were glad to have that Roman out of their Queen's life.

10

Cleopatra Gets Married

The whole palace at Alexandria was buzzing. In the kitchen, the cooks talked about it. Out on the grounds, the gardeners talked about it. People stopped in the streets to talk about it. Antony had left Rome. He was heading East. He was going to war in the East. Would he visit Egypt? Would Cleopatra speak to him?

Antony had spent four long years in Rome with Octavia. She was the perfect wife. She did everything right. She was beautiful. She always smiled. She was sweet and kind. And she was about as exciting as a turtle. Antony could not

67

stand it another minute. He talked to Octavian about going fighting. After all, Antony was a general. He could take more countries for Rome.

Antony left Rome without looking back. He was never to see his city again. He made his way East, until he came to Syria. His friend Dellius was with him. Antony said to Dellius one day, "We are so close to Egypt. I can almost hear Cleopatra's musical voice. I must see her. I must at least explain."

"If you have a drinking problem, you don't pour drinks to look at. Know what I mean?" Dellius said.

Antony knew. But he already could not help himself. He needed a drink from the cup of Egypt. He sent one of his men to Alexandria.

"Cleopatra, there is a Roman here with a message," Charmian said.

"I can guess who sent him," Cleopatra said. "I wish Antony would stay out of my life." But she went to hear what the Roman had to say.

"I have a message for you," Antony's man said.

"I'm sure you do," Cleopatra replied.

The Roman was taking brown paper off something on the floor. Then he laid this something at Cleopatra's feet. It was a new fishing pole. Hanging on the fishing line was a beautiful piece of cloth. It was a kind of cloth made only in Rome. It had pictures of little fish all over it. The fish were sewn with real silver. The Roman said, "My master, Antony, invites you to come to Syria. He said to tell you there is good fishing there."

Cleopatra had to laugh at Antony's gift. He knew her so well. She knew she would go to see him. She could not help herself. "Charmian," she called, "look what they are catching in Syria. We can't pass up fishing like this." So Cleopatra went to Syria.

When Cleopatra walked into the room, Antony could hardly stand up. His knees felt like water. "I didn't think I would ever see you again," he said. His voice shook.

"You almost never did," Cleopatra replied. She could see that Antony was still in love with her. But she had to be careful. She had been hurt once already. "You could have written when you got married," she said.

"I'm sorry. That marriage means nothing to me. I had to come back to you," Antony said. "I married Octavia to please Octavian. I didn't want to fight a war to keep my part of Rome. It was the only thing I could do," Antony explained. "I don't love Octavia. You must know that. I love you, Cleopatra. I have never loved anyone but you, my Egypt."

"Well I love you too, you terrible Roman. I wish I didn't—but I do," Cleopatra said. "What are we going to do?"

Antony thought for a long time. It was quiet in the room. Antony wanted to be happy. He was getting old. He loved Cleopatra more than anything—even more than Rome. "I never thought it would come to this," Antony said at last. "If I must decide on Rome or Egypt then I take Egypt. I am going to divorce Octavia. I am going to marry you."

Cleopatra knew how they talked about her in Rome. She knew they called her names. So this tasted sweet! She would rule the Eastern half of the Roman Empire with Antony. Secretly she thought maybe she would rule the whole Roman Empire some day. She would return Rome to Caesar through his son. Caesarion could be heir to Rome as well as to the Egyptian crown. Besides all this, she would marry the man she loved.

When Dellius heard what Antony had done, he could not believe it. "My friend," he said to Antony, "this is no way to please Octavian. There will be a war. Romans will fight Romans over this Egyptian Queen."

Antony no longer cared if Romans fought Romans. He was in love. He went to Alexandria. Antony and Cleopatra were married.

11

Antony and Cleopatra in Egypt

As soon as they were married, Antony gave Cleopatra several countries to rule. Now Egypt ruled more land than anyone in Cleopatra's family had ever ruled. And Cleopatra had taken this land without a war! Her people were very pleased. Even the learned men were pleased at Egypt's new power.

The learned men soon had something else to be pleased about. Antony brought 200,000 books to Egypt. He ordered a new library to be built in Alexandria. He knew how much Cleopatra missed the library that burned during the war. What a perfect gift for Cleopatra.

Antony and Cleopatra started out ruling the East together. Cleopatra liked having Antony help her rule. It made things easier for her. He made sure her orders were carried out. But slowly Cleopatra had to decide more and more things by herself. Antony was spending more and more time just having fun. He went out to parties and drinking most nights. Cleopatra's life began to swing up and down. One minute she felt like she was on top of the world. The next minute she felt like she was at the bottom. Never before had her feelings changed so quickly.

Back in Rome, they said Cleopatra was slowly killing Antony. The Romans heard about all the parties. Stories that were not even true reached Rome. They talked about Cleopatra, the witch, again. No one seemed to see that Antony was wearing Cleopatra down. The Romans were used to thinking bad things about Cleopatra. So it was easy for them to see things the wrong way around.

When she was happy during these years, Cleopatra felt great. She was still a fine ruler and a good queen. When Antony was happy, no one could keep him down. He was a lot of fun. But Cleopatra started to catch herself wishing he would grow up. As the years went by, Cleopatra's love for Antony was not so fierce. In fact, it began to disappear bit by bit. She still loved him—but not as much. Antony was 15 years older than Cleopatra. And she didn't like the way he was growing old. He was not growing wise. He was growing lazy and mindless.

Even though her feelings for Antony changed, Cleopatra never thought of leaving him. She was the kind of person who stood by her friends. Besides, she still cared about him a lot. There was even more to it than that. Over the years she had presented him with three children. First there were the twins—a boy and a girl. Then, a few years later, Antony and Cleopatra had another son. Antony had also become the Roman father Caesarion never had. Caesarion was ten years old when Antony married Cleopatra. With his stories, Antony made Caesar live again for Caesarion. Antony spent a lot of time with these children. Cleopatra could not help but love him for being such a good father.

During these few years, Antony and Cleopatra didn't think much about Octavian. Many people said that Antony should have gone to war with Octavian now. Octavian was not ready to fight Antony at this time. But Antony didn't feel like fighting Octavian. Things might have been different if he had.

Octavian was still angry that Antony had left Octavia. He was also angry that Antony was letting that woman rule the East. Octavian already didn't like Cleopatra. But the thing that bothered him the most was Caesarion. Caesarion was growing up quickly. Octavian was worried. Maybe Antony and Cleopatra would use their power for Caesarion. Maybe they would try to take Rome away from Octavian in Caesarion's name.

Octavian decided he wanted to start a war against Cleopatra. This was hard because Antony was her husband. The Roman people still respected Antony. They didn't like what he had done to Octavia. But most of the Romans didn't want to fight a war over it.

Then Antony made a big mistake. He wanted everyone to know that Cleopatra was the Queen of the East. He wanted everyone to know that Cleopatra's children would rule one day. So Antony threw a giant party in Alexandria. He made all the rulers from the Eastern countries come. It was the kind of party Egypt had become known for. At this party, Antony put gold crowns on Cleopatra and her children. He made everyone bow down to them. He said Cleopatra owned the Eastern Roman Empire. When Octavian heard about this, it was the final blow. Even the Romans who liked Antony thought this was too much. Antony had just given away half the Roman Empire! The Romans could not believe it.

Octavian acted fast while the Romans were angry. He sent a message to Cleopatra saying Rome and Egypt were at war. Octavian would not give up half the Roman Empire without a fight.

Antony was very angry too. He had fought hard to win the Eastern countries in the first place. He had spent his life fighting. These countries belonged to Rome to begin with because of Antony. If he wanted to let his wife rule these lands, he would! If he wanted to give these lands to his children, he would! Octavian had not earned these lands. Antony had.

Antony started to prepare for war. His men loved him and would follow him into any war. But they felt funny about this war. Antony's men were Roman. They would be fighting fellow Romans. Antony had to try to make them feel better about this.

Antony had another problem too. Cleopatra wanted to go fighting with him. Antony was the greatest general living. He knew that it would be a mistake for Cleopatra to go fighting. She knew a lot of things; but she didn't know much about war. He could not make her change her mind, though. What is more, she wanted to fight at sea. She was readying 60 Egyptian ships.

Antony's men were not very good at fighting on the water in ships. He had never trained them for that. They could fight very well on land. So Antony wanted to let Octavian try to take over Alexandria. Then, when Octavian's men marched into Egypt, Antony could fight them on land.

Egyptians liked to fight from ships. Cleopatra's men were trained for war at sea. And Cleopatra saw this as an Egyptian war. This was a big mistake on her part. Antony was a great general. So Cleopatra should have let him fight the way he felt comfortable. But once Octavian started the war, Cleopatra was never the same. She would not listen to Antony's ideas about the coming fight. She had been deciding so many things herself lately. She had not asked what Antony thought about things for a long time.

Antony could see that more talk was useless. Cleopatra's mind was made up. So Antony prepared to fight Octavian at sea. Cleopatra would be at the fight as she wanted to be.

Octavian was happy to hear that Antony was preparing to fight at sea. Octavian's men were trained to fight from ships. He knew Antony's men were not trained for this. So Octavian sailed for Egypt right away.

Antony and Cleopatra were eating breakfast one morning. Dellius came with a message. "Octavian has left Rome," Dellius said. "He is on his way East."

"I am not ready to fight yet!" Antony cried. "I am expecting more men from the Kings of the East."

"Don't worry," Cleopatra said. "You have

my men. They are ready to fight."

Antony spoke without thinking. "But Egypt has not fought a war for almost 20 years!"

"What are you trying to say about Egypt?" Cleopatra asked angrily.

Antony looked at the floor. He said nothing. "We will be ready to sail within the week," Cleopatra said.

"You have changed," Antony said. "Ever since I put that gold crown on your head. Something has been different."

"Ever since you put that crown on my head?!" Cleopatra cried. "I was born with a crown on my head."

Antony's mouth fell open. "Yes, but you were Queen of Egypt. It was I who made you Queen of the East. I earned all these lands by fighting for them. You are Queen of the East because you are my wife."

"I think we are on edge because of the war," Cleopatra said. "We will feel a lot better when we beat Octavian."

"Maybe you are right," Antony replied. He was tired of thinking. He was tired of fighting.

If only Octavian would let him alone. He was happy in Egypt with Cleopatra and his children.

Meanwhile, Cleopatra was having some other thoughts. What if Egypt owned the whole Roman Empire? She could run the Empire from Egypt. She would move the thinkers and leaders of Rome to Alexandria. This was her big chance. She imagined the new Egyptian Empire. And Caesarion would one day rule Rome and Egypt. Caesar would have liked this. No woman had ever been this close to taking over the Roman Empire. But Cleopatra was not just any woman.

Before she left Alexandria, Cleopatra gave Apollodorus some secret orders. There was a monument to the Kings and Queens in Cleopatra's family. It was in the palace gardens. It was several stories tall. It had a strong stone gate at the bottom. You could lock it from the inside. She told Apollodorus to take all the Egyptian treasures from the palace. She said he should put them into the monument. "Anything that is worth anything—put it in the monument," she said. "I want all of Egypt's treasure safely stored in the monument. If we don't win the war, I will get to the monument somehow. I will burn the treasures of Egypt. I will keep these treasures from Octavian."

Apollodorus promised to do as he was told. He took Cleopatra's hand. "You must win this war, my Queen. Egypt is lost without you."

The night before she went to war, Cleopatra called Caesarion to her. He was a beautiful, strong boy. He was already 16 years old. Cleopatra had started to ask for his ideas about ruling Egypt. He was so like Caesar sometimes. He thought about everything too much, just like Caesar. That night Cleopatra told him to leave Egypt for his safety. At first he didn't want to go. But she talked him into it. "Octavian will kill you if you give him the chance," Cleopatra told him. She made plans for Caesarion to go to India. He was to stay there until the war ended.

Hundreds of Egyptians went to the shore to see Antony and Cleopatra leave. The Queen was going to war. There was one thought Cleopatra could not get out of her mind. The Roman Empire could become the Egyptian Empire. Very soon, Egypt could be the greatest country in the world. Then Cleopatra would leave this country to Caesarion.

12
War

"Octavian's ships are a few miles from here," Dellius said. "It only took an hour to row back here from them." Dellius had just come from looking at Octavian's ships. The war was about to start.

"I want you to stay here with your Egyptian ships," Antony told Cleopatra. "I promise I will send for you if I need you. Let Octavian fight with my men first. I will wear him out. Then I will send for you. Your men will be fresh. They will have a good chance of finishing Octavian off."

Antony had fought many wars. So Cleopatra

decided to follow his plan. She was willing to stay behind for now.

It was early in the day. Gold light from the morning sun jumped in and out of the waves. Antony remembered that he had first met Cleopatra on a ship. He had fallen in love with her the minute he saw her. And now he was fighting his own countrymen because of her. It was strange the way things worked out.

"So, my Roman, are you ready to go?" Cleopatra asked.

Antony jumped. She had come up behind him and surprised him. "Yes, Egypt, I'm ready," Antony said. There was something different about Cleopatra. She looked frightening. She looked like a snake when it is about to strike. She looked dangerous. Antony wanted to tell her he loved her before he went to war. But he was afraid of her. "I'll send you a message," he said to her.

"You are my husband," Cleopatra said. "You must win for Egypt as well as for Rome."

Antony had many things inside him to say. But he said nothing. Instead he turned and went to war.

Cleopatra walked back and forth on the ship. Charmian brought her some food. Cleopatra was not hungry. She could not even sit down. She was too restless.

In the afternoon the sounds of fighting rang out across the water. Octavian and Antony had moved nearer to Cleopatra's ships. She could see some of the fighting now. No message had come from Antony yet. Cleopatra was finding it harder and harder to wait. What if Antony had been killed? Suddenly she imagined Antony dead a hundred different ways. She decided to get a better look at the fighting.

Up to this point things were still almost even. Antony's men were doing surprisingly well. Octavian was not a great general yet. He would be one day. But he was still young. Antony had been a great general for many years. His men were holding their own. Octavian had burned several of Antony's ships. But Antony was by no means losing. Who can say what would have happened if Cleopatra had stayed back? But she didn't stay back. She had to see what was happening. Her whole life rested on the outcome of this war.

Cleopatra sailed up to the fighting with her 60 shining new ships. They had lots of gold and silver on them. Her sails were all different colors. Cleopatra had always been a show stopper. But this worked against her today. Everyone stopped fighting.

Octavian gave an order that he didn't want Cleopatra killed. So his men backed off from Cleopatra's ship. In fact, they backed off from all her ships. Then the strangest thing happened. Cleopatra and her ships sailed straight through the fight untouched. No one knows for sure what went on at that moment. No one fought at all.

Cleopatra had never seen a war close up. But now she saw Antony's burning ships. Most of the men had jumped off them. Many of them were still swimming and calling for help. Many of them were burned. Men lay dying on all the ships. She heard their screams. She could see some of them. Cleopatra had watched many prisoners put to death. But that was the law. There was an order to that. This war had no order. Anything could happen. It seemed to Cleopatra that the gods themselves stayed out of men's wars. A war had nothing to do with the

Egypt and Rome fight at sea.

stars. It made no sense. Cleopatra was more frightened than she had ever been in her life. She ordered her ships to run back to Egypt. She was too frightened to think.

Antony wondered what had happened. Was something wrong? What was Cleopatra trying to tell him? Antony stopped thinking like a general. He was thinking like a man in love instead. All kinds of thoughts raced through his head. Why had Cleopatra sailed when Antony had told her to wait for a message? Why was she running away?

Octavian's men had forgotten they were at war for a second. They watched Cleopatra's beautiful ships sail by. But once Cleopatra was sailing away, Octavian's men started fighting again.

Antony wondered why Octavian let Cleopatra's ships sail through untouched. Could Cleopatra have made some kind of plan with Octavian? Antony jumped into a small boat. He took Dellius and a few men with him. He headed after Cleopatra. He had to get to the bottom of this. Not many people saw Antony leave. Octavian didn't see him leave. As the fighting continued behind him, Antony followed Cleopatra.

Soon, one of Cleopatra's men spotted Antony in his boat. Cleopatra waited for him to catch up with her. "What were you doing out there?" Antony asked angrily.

"I got scared." Cleopatra told him. "Who asked you to follow me?"

"You got scared?!" Antony yelled. "Do you think I will believe that? Cleopatra got scared?! You have joined up with Octavian, right?"

Cleopatra could not believe her ears. She became very angry. "How could you think I would do anything that low? I am a queen. I don't play sides. I certainly don't play sides against my husband."

Antony walked to the front of Cleopatra's ship. He sat down and refused to speak. Cleopatra refused to speak to him too.

While Antony and Cleopatra were sailing back to Egypt, the war continued. As night fell, word spread among Antony's men—Antony was gone. He had gone back to Egypt. Without a general, Antony's men were afraid to fight. They were Romans. So was Octavian. Antony's men sent a message to Octavian. They didn't want to keep fighting. Many of them wanted to go home to Rome. They were tired of Egypt. This news pleased Octavian. He took Antony's men in. He decided to sail to Egypt and take over Alexandria. Octavian could not know what terrible sights awaited him in Alexandria. Antony and Cleopatra were like two giant stars falling from the sky.

13
A Death in Egypt

Cleopatra's ships sailed all the way to Alexandria. Charmian and Dellius talked to Cleopatra and Antony. They made them stop fighting with each other. They talked them into at least speaking to each other. But they continued to be cold to one another.

Antony had lost all his men and his ships. He still had Cleopatra's ships, though. So when they got to Alexandria, Antony prepared to fight in Cleopatra's ships.

As soon as Cleopatra's ship got to Alexandria, she hurried to the palace. She called for Apollodorus. "Are the treasures in the monument?" she asked him.

"Yes, my Queen," Apollodorus replied. "What has happened?"

"We are losing the war," Cleopatra answered. She took Charmian and went into the monument. She had her servants bring her some things from the palace. Then Cleopatra made her home in the monument. She locked the heavy stone door at the bottom. She would not come out.

Meanwhile, Antony was waiting at the waterfront for Octavian. But before Octavian came, he sent a man with a message. This man would not speak to Antony. He said his message was for the Queen. So Antony took him to Cleopatra's monument home. Cleopatra opened the door and let Octavian's man in.

When Cleopatra was alone with this man, he bowed before her. "Queen of Egypt, Octavian sends this respectful message. If you turn Antony over to Octavian then you will be safe. Octavian promises to care for you and your children. You may keep the crown of Egypt," the man said.

Cleopatra didn't believe these words for a

second. Why should Octavian care about Cleopatra? Besides, she was not about to turn her husband over to his enemy. "What kind of woman does Octavian think I am? I will not feed my husband to the lions to keep my crown. Tell Octavian that. Now leave."

This man took Cleopatra's hand and bent down low. He then stood and turned to leave. Antony was standing in the doorway. Antony had not heard what had been said. He just came in when this man took Cleopatra's hand. Antony became as angry as a great tiger. He beat the man up on the spot. Then he took him back to the waterfront. He threw him back into his boat. "Take that message back to Octavian," Antony said.

Antony returned to the monument. Cleopatra had locked the door again. Antony kicked at the door. He yelled, "If you have made plans with Octavian, I will kill you." He was sure she had gone to Octavian behind his back. She had loved Caesar when he ruled Rome. Then she had loved Antony when he became a ruler. Now she probably thought Octavian would win so she had joined with him. Antony was angry and scared. He forgot all the good years he had spent with Cleopatra. But he still loved her fiercely. His love made him imagine all kinds of things now. And he was too angry to think things through.

Cleopatra was too angry to speak to Antony. When he left the monument, Cleopatra came out and called Apollodorus. "I must speak to you of terrible things," she said to him. "If Octavian comes I will kill myself and burn the Egyptian treasures. Now I must talk to you about my children. When my father died he asked you to protect me. I was a little girl. You have been more than my protection. You have been like family to one who had no family. Now I ask you to do the same for my children. Look after them should anything happen to me. Protect them. Teach them who their mother is. Especially look out for Caesarion. He is safe in India. One day maybe he can return. One day maybe he will fight Octavian and win."

Apollodorus was a big, strong man, but tears ran down his face. "Your son will always have a friend in me," Apollodorus said. "But why do you talk as if all is lost?"

"The gods have turned away from me. I can feel them gone. My star reader has run away.

He probably fears to tell me what he sees in the sky. I am prepared for death." Cleopatra closed the heavy door to the monument again. She locked it carefully behind her.

Apollodorus returned to the palace. Other servants and Egyptian leaders wanted to know what was happening. Apollodorus told them the Queen was preparing for death. The news spread across Alexandria. Soon it spread to Cleopatra's men on her ships at the waterfront. Her men didn't know what to do. Antony was walking back and forth on the shore. He was talking to himself. He was waving his arms around. The Egyptian fighters thought he had lost his mind. Maybe he had. Should they follow his orders?

Just then Octavian's ships appeared in the distance. Cleopatra's Egyptian generals decided to talk to Octavian before fighting. So they sailed out to meet him. They lifted their oars as a signal. This signal meant they were not about to fight. When Antony saw the Egyptian ships signal Octavian, he sent Cleopatra a message.

Dellius appeared below the window of Cleopatra's monument. He called up to her.

"Antony wishes me to tell you he knows what you have done. He knows you have joined with Octavian. Rome has no more respect for Egypt. Antony says," Dellius stopped speaking for a minute. "I am under orders to say this. Antony says he has as much respect for Cleopatra as for a dog."

When Cleopatra heard these words she saw red. How could Antony think such things of her, his wife, a queen?! They had been through so much together.

"Charmian," Cleopatra said, "go to the window. Tell Dellius that upon hearing these words I have killed myself. Tell him that I have always loved Antony. Tell him that what Antony thinks is not true. Say that his unjust words have taken away my will to live." Cleopatra wanted to hurt Antony as much as he had hurt her.

When Dellius returned to Antony, he found him roaring like a dragon. His voice pounded out across the sea. "How could she?!"

"The Queen is dead," Dellius said.

Antony stopped in his tracks. His anger disappeared.

"She says that your words are unjust. She

said to tell you that she has always loved you. Your words have taken away her will to live. Cleopatra has died for love of Antony." Dellius hated to bring these terrible messages back and forth.

When Antony heard this news, he howled like a trapped wolf. A great man was broken in that moment. Antony cried, "With Cleopatra gone, I have lost everything." Then he stabbed himself before Dellius could stop him. Dellius quickly called for help. He had Antony brought to the palace.

When Apollodorus saw what had happened, he rushed off to Cleopatra. "Cleopatra," he called outside the monument. "Come to the window to speak to Apollodorus."

The closest window to the ground was three stories up. Cleopatra's face appeared at this window.

"I have terrible news," Apollodorus said. "Antony believes that you are dead. He has stabbed himself."

Cleopatra gasped. Could this be true? She could not speak.

"Is he dead?" Charmian called down.

"He was still alive when I left him," Apollodorus replied.

"Then bring him here," Cleopatra ordered. "Tell him I am still alive. He must live."

Apollodorus returned to Antony. When Antony heard that Cleopatra was alive, he seemed to grow stronger. "Now I will see her face once more before I die," Antony said.

Apollodorus and Dellius carried Antony to the monument. Cleopatra's servants and many other Egyptians poured into the garden behind them. Many people were crying. No one could believe these terrible things were happening.

Cleopatra didn't know when Octavian would get to Egypt. At this point, she feared being taken prisoner by Octavian more than anything. She did not want to die in Rome as a prisoner of war. If she must die, she wanted to die at home—in Egypt. Octavian might appear at any minute. So Cleopatra was afraid to come out of the monument.

Cleopatra threw ropes down from her window. She had Apollodorus tie the ropes around her dying husband. Then Cleopatra and Charmian pulled at the ropes with all their might. Antony reached his arms up to Cleopatra with his last strength. It was the saddest sight.

When Cleopatra saw Antony reaching up to her, she started to cry. She had never had much of a family when she was growing up. Egypt was her life. This man had loved her deeply. He had given her a family. He had given up his country for the love of her. Now he had given up his life. Cleopatra remembered how much she loved Antony.

When Cleopatra pulled Antony through the window she carefully laid him down. "My King, my husband," she said softly. "I have not loved you well. It is Cleopatra who has taken Antony's life. Now my life is not worth a bit of dust."

"Don't say these things," Antony replied. "You have loved me very well. It is I who have not loved you well. How could I have thought such terrible things about my Egypt? You gave me my happiest years. I am glad to die of love for Cleopatra."

"I should never have sailed through the fighting like that," Cleopatra exclaimed. "What were you to think?"

"I should not have followed you," Antony

replied. "No general in his right mind would do such a thing."

"Why did I send you that message that I was dead? I should not have been so quick to anger," Cleopatra said.

"But I was so quick to anger myself," Antony replied.

"Everything moved so quickly. There was no time to think. We almost had the world in our hands. But we didn't listen to each other. If only we had listened. Now I have killed you," Cleopatra cried. She held Antony in her arms.

"But you have also loved me." Antony said. "People will say that we lost the world because of our love. But it is a world well lost. These years with you were worth more than the world to me. I am dying, Egypt. I want you to know something. You are the only woman I have ever loved. My Cleopatra." With these words, Antony died. The blows of love had killed one of the greatest generals who ever lived. He had loved Cleopatra and he didn't want to live without her. Antony had been a man who did what he wanted to do. He said whatever he wanted to say. He made his life the way he wanted it to be. This can't be said about many people.

14

Octavian's Plans

Cleopatra's sadness can hardly be told in words. She put a blanket around Antony. Then she held him for a long time. For once, Cleopatra had no plans. People called up from the garden outside. Cleopatra didn't move. She forgot all of Antony's failings. All she knew was that she had loved him and he had died.

Charmian went to the window. She called down the news of Antony's death. Cleopatra just sat there. For a long time Cleopatra and Charmian didn't move. They heard voices and loud noises outside. But inside the monument time stood still. Cleopatra was remembering her life with Antony. She remembered him following her back to Alexandria from Tarsus. She thought of the time she put that smoked fish on his line. She remembered Antony chasing their children around the trees in the garden. He had taught Caesarion how to shoot a bow and arrow. She could almost hear Antony laughing. How long would she be able to remember the sound of that laugh? How long could she remember the exact way he smiled?

Suddenly a face appeared at the window. Cleopatra jumped up. There was a man at the top of a ladder. Cleopatra tried to knock him down. But it was too late. He was strong. He climbed in. More men came in after him. They were Romans. Cleopatra had forgotten about Octavian. Now she had let herself become Octavian's prisoner.

Then one man said, "Prepare to meet Octavian."

"Have some respect for the Queen," Charmian exclaimed. "Can't you see her husband has just died? We will be in the next room preparing to meet Octavian." Charmian took Cleopatra by the arm and led her through the door.

When they were alone in the next room, Charmian shook Cleopatra. "You are still the Queen of Egypt," Charmian said. "You have made Egypt great. The Romans are scared to death of you. You have years and years to be sad that Antony has died. But now you must snap out of this. You must think fast. You must be smart. You must save Egypt."

"I am tired of saving Egypt," Cleopatra said. "I have spent my life saving Egypt, working for Egypt. I have worn a heavy crown since the day I was born. I wish I could go to sleep beside Antony and never wake up."

"But Egypt is counting on you," Charmian said.

"I have already lost Egypt," Cleopatra said. Then Cleopatra put on a straight, white dress. Her face was washed clean with crying. She took off all her silver and gold. She put it on a table. She piled some of her family treasures on the table too. She knew how much Octavian loved money. She also knew Octavian was a forthright man. She would have to be sure to be straightforward with him.

When Octavian entered the room, he was very surprised. He had heard so many stories about Cleopatra. He expected someone very different. He found a tall, thin woman seated on a low chair. She was not beautiful the way he thought she would be. She spoke quietly in a beautiful, musical voice. Octavian had planned to say some terrible things to Cleopatra. But now he felt sorry to see so great a woman brought so low.

"On this table you will find some gifts for you. I have many more treasures in this monument. You may have them all," Cleopatra said. "These things are worthless to me."

"Why do you want to give away the treasures of your family?" Octavian wondered what Cleopatra was up to.

"You would take them from me anyway. It is better to give them as a gift," Cleopatra replied. "This way people will speak of the respect Cleopatra showed Octavian."

Octavian had imagined Cleopatra would try to trick him. He thought he had to be careful. But she was so straightforward. She seemed sad and wise.

"You are looking at a queen who has failed her people. Her husband has just died. Now a great empire is about to swallow up her country. What use do these treasures have for me now? You are the ruler of a country. Just as I am. You and I, we have no life of our own. I can't remember deciding anything for myself without first thinking of Egypt. If there is anything I can do to keep Egypt then tell me. If not, then let me die."

Octavian was not sure what he wanted to do. He had a hard time staying angry at this woman. In fact, he could not help liking her. He certainly didn't want her dead. She was quite different from what he expected. In everything she did and said, she was very respectful of Octavian. And there was something about her. He could not put his finger on it. It was like a fire burning in her being. He could not take his eyes off her.

Octavian decided he wanted to take her back to Rome. He would take her back as a prisoner. She would be quite a prize to bring back from the war. But he would be good to her. He would show her his respect. He thought she might be very helpful to him one day.

"I can't let you kill yourself," Octavian said. "You are too great a woman. I will take you back to Rome with me."

How Cleopatra had feared this! She didn't want to die in Rome as a prisoner. She didn't want to die far away from Egypt! She had an idea. "At least let me bury my husband," she said. "He should be given the funeral of a great man. He was the King of Egypt. He was a great Roman general and ruler." She needed time to find a way to end her life in Egypt. Besides, she really did want to give Antony a beautiful funeral.

Octavian saw no harm in letting Cleopatra bury Antony. Antony had been a great Roman leader. He should be given the funeral of a great man.

"I will wait until Antony is buried to leave for Rome," Octavian said.

15
The Final Days

Cleopatra planned Antony's funeral from her rooms in the monument. Octavian kept her there as his prisoner. He had her looked after very well. All her needs were met. But Octavian's men kept a close eye on her. They didn't want her to kill herself. Octavian also had Cleopatra's children looked after. Octavian was secretly very disappointed to find Caesarion gone. He had wanted to kill him.

Charmian was held as a prisoner with Cleopatra. But Apollodorus was still able to go where he pleased. Octavian had not figured out how close Apollodorus was to the Queen.

He thought Apollodorus was just another servant. So Octavian's men didn't pay close attention to Apollodorus. That is why Cleopatra was able to get a message to Apollodorus.

One day Apollodorus was ordered to Cleopatra's rooms. Cleopatra gave him a rolled up paper. "I have written down everything which Antony would want buried with him. Take this paper to Octavian," Cleopatra said. Then she whispered quickly, "Read it first." She whispered to him in the wink of an eye. No one noticed. But Apollodorus heard her whisper.

As soon as Apollodorus left the monument he hid behind a tree. He opened the paper. Rolled up with the message for Octavian, he found this message:

Apollodorus—You must find a way to bring me a poisonous snake. An asp is the best poisonous snake. A bite from an asp would be a quick and easy death. After Antony's funeral, bring me an asp. Find a way! Thank you and goodbye my dear Apollodorus.

"I will find a way, my Queen," Apollodorus said.

Antony's funeral was large and beautiful. Romans and Egyptians stood together to pay their last respects. Kings came from Eastern countries. Cleopatra stood proud with her three children. It was the last time her people would see her. She was not wearing any gold or silver. Except she had a thin piece of gold around her head. Her eyes and her hair still flashed. A fire still burned within her. She was still the Queen.

As she returned to the monument, she thought of Antony. At least she had given him a king's funeral. How strange it would be if she must die in Antony's Rome. And now Antony was laid to rest in her Egypt.

The morning after the funeral, Apollodorus brought a basket to Cleopatra. He showed Octavian's men the fruit in the basket. "Here is a little gift to make the Queen feel better. It is from her servants. May I bring her this fruit?" Apollodorus asked. Octavian's men looked at the fruit carefully. They even made Apollodorus eat a piece. It looked harmless. They would not let Apollodorus take the basket in. But a Roman took it to Cleopatra. He told her it was a gift from her servants.

Cleopatra is remembered as one of the world's strongest and great queens.

As soon as the Roman left, Cleopatra ran to the window. Apollodorus waved goodbye to her from the ground. She knew what she would find in the bottom of the basket. And she was right. Under the fruit there was a piece of cloth. Inside the cloth there was an asp.

Octavian was preparing to leave for Rome when he was given a note. The note said: "Please look after my children and bury me with Antony." It was signed by Cleopatra. It didn't take Octavian long to figure out what was going on. He raced to Cleopatra's monument. But he was already too late.

When Octavian's men entered Cleopatra's room, she was already dead. She was laid out in her most queenly clothes. She wore the crown of Egypt on her head. Charmian lay dying at her feet.

"What have you done?" one of Octavian's men cried.

"Is this not a good death for a great woman? Is this not the death of a queen?" Charmian asked with her last breath.

After Cleopatra's death, Octavian took over Egypt. He sent his men to find Caesarion. They tracked him down in India. Octavian had him killed. But Octavian took Antony's three Egyptian children to Rome in safety. There his kind sister Octavia raised them with love. When Cleopatra's daughter grew up she married an African king. So she became a queen in her own right.

Cleopatra was buried with Antony as she had wished. She was 39 years old when she died. The year was 30 B.C. She was given the funeral of a great woman. She was indeed great. She had held the attention and imagination of two great rulers of Rome. Her every word and move was told throughout the Roman Empire. She was feared, respected and loved—everyone felt something for Cleopatra. She had made the world stand up and take notice of Egypt. She had protected Egypt during a time when other countries fell to Rome. She ruled Egypt and other countries during times when women ruled very little. And she, a woman, had nearly brought the Roman Empire to its knees. The Egyptian people thought of her as a daughter of the gods. Cleopatra, the last Queen of Egypt, left her mark on the world.